Pumpkin Pie and Puddles

Poems for every day

Pumpkin Pie and Puddles

Poems for every day

Georgie Adams

Illustrated by Selina Young

Dolphin

For Sally, Lydia, Freya and Dominic
With love   G.A.

This collection first published in Great Britain in 1999
by Orion Children's Books
a division of the Orion Publishing Group Ltd
Orion House
5 Upper St Martin's Lane
London WC2H 9EA

Poems in this collection have been selected from
A Year Full of Stories,
first published by Orion Children's Books in 1997

A catalogue record for this book
is available from the British Library

Printed in Great Britain by The Guernsey Press Co Ltd
Guernsey, Channel Islands

ISBN 1 85881 718 8

Contents

What a Rumpus!
26. I've Heard
27. Listen
28. Breakfast Time
29. Making Music
30. Noisy Dora

Come Rain or Shine
32. Weather Reports
33. Summertime
34. A Good Rainy Day
35. Too Hot
35. My New Umbrella
36. Rainbows
37. How Does the Wind Blow?
38. Puddles

All About Me
8. Bathtime
9. My Real Birthday
10. All About Me
11. A Little Monkey
12. Things I Can Do
13. All in a Day
14. Nobody Wants Me

Play Time
16. Mud
17. Clay Play
18. My Sand Castle
19. Granny's Teddy Bear
20. Pretending
21. Clap Your Hands
22. My Chair Bus
24. Nurse Jill

Let's Count!
40. One, Two, Off to the Zoo
42. Twenty Knobbly Knees
43. A Big Sum
44. Busy Bees
45. Speckly Hen
46. Ten Little Monkeys
48. Small Things
50. Pumpkin Pie

Furry Friends

52. New Chicks
53. Three Out Walking
54. The Chase
55. Pets at the Vet
56. Aristotle Humphrey Miller
57. My New Puppy
57. Prehistoric Pet
58. Hunt the Guinea Pig

At School

60. The Way to School
61. Team Games
62. Sports Day
63. A Quiet Corner
64. School Rules
65. The School Play
66. Dinosaur Spellings

A Scary Bunch

68. The Giant
70. Under My Bed
71. A Monstrous Recipe
72. Ghost Train
73. My Secret Monster
74. Spotted Shingly
    Shangly Beasts

75. I Know A Tumbly House
76. Green-eyed Witches

Plain Silly!

78. Ladywig and Earbird
79. Colourful Moods
80. Saturday Sweets
81. The Queen of Hearts
82. Tooth Fairies
83. Jumpy Custard
84. Bathroom Nonsense
85. Roger the Robot
86. Little Miss Locket

The World Around Us

88. A Colourful World
89. Globe Trotting
90. Opposites
91. How High is the Sky?
92. Big Things
93. Things People Do
94. On the Move
95. Circles
96. A Crumb

All About Me

Bathtime

In goes the water,
Not too hot.
Squeeze out the bubble stuff,
In goes the lot.

In goes my whale
In goes my boat.
In go all the toys
That I can float.

Now my bath is ready
What else can there be?
I think I remember ...
In goes ME!

My Real Birthday

Birthdays come round once a year
That's not quite true of mine.
My birthday falls in Leap Year
On February twenty-nine.

Four years ago, when I was born
My life had just begun.
This is my FIRST real birthday
But I am four — not one.

I have a birthday every year
So I grow up on time.
But my real one's every four years,
On February twenty-nine.

All About Me

I've got ...

A head for nodding, shaking and thinking,
Eyes for seeing, closing and blinking.

Ears for hearing nice things and boring,
A nose for smelling, blowing and snoring.

A mouth for speaking, eating and kissing,
Teeth for chewing — my front tooth is missing.

Arms for waving, hugging and squeezing,
Hands for clapping, helping and pleasing.

Elbows and knees for bending and stretching,
Legs for kicking, running and fetching.

And right at the bottom my two little feet
For dancing and tapping a musical beat.

A Little Monkey

I,

Sing like a bird

Swim like a fish

Kick like a donkey

Run like a hare

Eat like a pig

Sleep like a sloth

Leap like a frog

Climb like a bear

And sometimes ...

I'm just a little monkey.

Things I Can Do

I can ...
Stand on my head,
Touch my toes,
Do up my buttons and
Tie my bows.
Help with the shopping,
Feed the birds,
Choose my own books and
Read little words.
Splash in my bath,
Climb the stairs,
Kneel at my bedside and
Say my prayers.

All in a Day

What can you do in a day?

Wake in the morning,
Wash and dress.
Eat your breakfast — make a mess.
Paint your face,
Dance and sing,
Fish in the pond with a stick and string.
Feed the ducks,
Go for a walk,
Draw a picture with a piece of chalk.
Scrub your hands,
Have some tea,
Watch a programme on T.V.
Read a book,
Hop into bed ...
Dream all night, you sleepyhead!

Nobody Wants Me

1. Nobody wants me
   I'm leaving home.
   I'll be like a hermit
   And live on my own.

2. I could sleep in a tent
   In a dry desert land,
   And ride on a camel
   Across the hot sand.

3. I could go to the North Pole
   To live on the ice,
   And play with a polar bear —
   That would be nice!

4. Or find a deep jungle
   And live in a tree,
   With parrots and monkeys
   I'm sure they'd like me ...

5. But wait,
   Someone's calling
   I've got to go home.
   Somebody wants me
   I can't live alone.

6. There's Mum and my Dad and
   My sister, makes three.
   I really would miss them —
   And they would miss ME!

Play Time

Mud

There's a muddy little puddle
By the duckpond on our farm,
With squeedgy, squidgy mud in it
That trickles down my arm.
It squelches through my fingers,
And in between my toes;
I can't think how it happens
But mud gets up my nose.
My hair has sludgy lumps of it,
It splatters round my eyes ...
There's always loads of mud on **ME**
When I make my mud pies.

Clay Play

Roll it in a ball,
Stretch it if you can.
Squeeze it into arms and legs
To make a bendy man.

Roll it up again,
Now what will you make;
A pizza, car or aeroplane?
Oh no,
A wriggly snake!

My Sand Castle

I've made a castle out of sand
With towers and turrets — very grand,
And all around, a proper moat
Where I can float my sailing boat.

But when the tide has turned once more
And splashy waves roll to the shore,
I know the sea will wash away
The castle that I made today.

Granny's Teddy Bear

Granny says,
"My teddy bear is very old —
About a hundred years
And parts of him are bare and worn
Around his paws and ears.
His tummy once was round and fat,
Stuffed full of yellow straw,
It hasn't got much left of that —
He's thinner than before."

When she was young and Ted was new
They'd play for hours, you see.
Now we have fun together,
Gran's teddy bear and me.

Pretending

We're playing at doctors and nurses —
Austin has got a bad leg.
"I may have to cut it off with my saw,"
Says Melanie, shaking her head.

Edward says, "Look. I'm a dentist.
Here's a tooth that will have to come out.
You won't feel a thing, I'll pull it with string ...
Open wide and stop wriggling about!"

Clap Your Hands

Clap your hands when I say one,
Clap your hands and wiggle your tongue.
Nod your head when I say two,
Nod your head and touch your shoe.
Stamp your foot when I say three,
Stamp your foot and touch your knee.
Bend right over when I say four,
Bend right over and touch the floor!

My Chair Bus

Climb aboard my chair bus
There's room for all you bears.
Piggie can be the conductor,
Collecting all the fares.

First stop, the library
Then off to the shops and school;
Down and round by the football ground
And on to the swimming pool.

Now my bus is full up
So home without delay.
Everyone back to the toy box,
No more rides today!

Nurse Jill

Nurse come quick!
Teddy's been sick
Dolly is looking quite pale.
Piggy's in bed with a very sore head
And Tiger's hurt his tail.

Nurse comes along
Sings them a song
Jokes and does the splits.
No need for a pill with nice Nurse Jill
She keeps the toys in fits!

What a Rumpus!

I've Heard

Lions **roar**,

bears **growl**,

horses **neigh**,

cows **moo**,

hens **cluck**,

ducks **quack**,

chicks **cheep**,

mice **squeak** ...

But I've never heard ants say **ANYTHING AT ALL**.

Listen!

Sirens **wail**
Cymbals **clash**
Doors **bang**
Waves **crash**.

Twigs **snap**
Plates **clatter**
Fires **crackle**
Children **chatter**.

Bees **hum**
Birds **sing**
Kettles **whistle**
Bells **ring**.

Cats **purr**
Locks **click**
Dreamers **sigh**
Clocks **tick … tick … tick …**

Breakfast Time

The juice in the mixer goes **wheee-wheee-whirr**.

The rice in my bowl goes **crickle-crackle-snap!**

The milk from the jug goes **splish-sploosh-splosh**.

The bacon in the pan goes **sizzle-fizzle-splat!**

The bell on the cooker goes **ping-ting-a-ping**.

The coffee in the pot goes **puff-poddle-pop!**

My teeth on the toast go **crunch-crunch-crunch**.

And Daddy in the car goes **peep-beep-parp!**

"It's time to go to school."

Making Music

Trill! goes the trumpet,

Twang! goes the harp,

Peep! goes the piccolo, shrill and sharp.

Clash! go the cymbals,

Clang! go the chimes,

Boom! goes the bass drum, umpteen times!

Noisy Dora

Noisy Dora
What a snorer!
How her friends in town implored her,
"Noisy Dora, please don't snore,
We can't stand it any more."

Noisy Dora
Didn't care,
Turned her nose up in the air.
Caused a rumpus and a riot,
"Noisy Dora, do be QUIET!"

The last I heard
And, quite by chance
Noisy Dora went to France.
So if you go there, do make sure
Noisy Dora's not next-door.

Come Rain or Shine

Weather Reports

"The weather will be warm today,
Sunny, fine and bright."

I poked my head outside the door.
The weather man was right.

"The weather will be wet today,
With rainy April showers."

I put my new umbrella up
And walked about for hours.

"There's going to be a storm today,
With thunder claps and lightning."

I curled up with my cat and dog.
Thunder storms are frightening.

"The weather will be ... weathery —
I'm not sure what to say."

Whatever the weather is going to do,
I'm going out to PLAY!

Summertime

Summer's coming,

Bees humming,

Flowers growing,

Rivers flowing,

Sun stronger,

Days longer,

Crickets playing,

Corn swaying,

Raindrops falling,

Songbirds calling … Summer's here!

A Good Rainy Day

A world without water —
What do you think?
No water to cook with,
Wash in or drink.

No puddles to splash in,
No rivers or seas;
No pools to go swimming
Whenever you please.

No rain for the garden,
For forests and crops.
All creatures need water —
Without it, life stops.

So the next time it rains
And its too wet to play,
Just say to yourself,
It's a good rainy day!

Too Hot

It's too hot to growl,
Too hot to purr,
Too hot to run, wriggle or stir.

But,

It's just right for sighing,
Dreaming and lying
Down by the pool
Where it's cool ... cool ... cool.

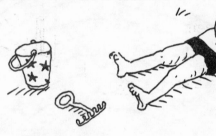

My New Umbrella

I've put my new umbrella up
To keep me from the rain,
But if the sun comes shining through ...
I'll put it down again!

Rainbows

When it's muddly sort of weather
With rain and sun together,
You may look, and way up high
See a rainbow in the sky.
And before it fades away
Name each colour — can you say?

Red orange yellow green blue indigo violet

How Does the Wind Blow?

How does the breeze blow,
Rustling all the leaves so?
It goes whispering by.

How does the wind blow,
Blowing round the house so?
It goes whistling by.

How does the storm blow,
Tossing all the ships so?
It goes roaring by!

Puddles

Town puddles
Street puddles
Soak through your feet puddles.
Cars whoosh through them
While we're waiting for the bus.

Farm puddles
Brown puddles
Gooey, squelchy warm puddles.
Ducks paddle in them
On flat webbed feet.

Rain puddles
Round puddles
Walking up and down puddles.
I splash through them
In my new rubber boots.

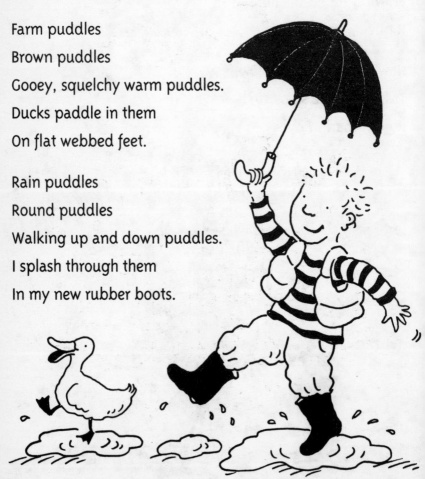

Let's Count

One, Two, Off to the Zoo

One, two
We're off to the zoo
Mummy is driving the car.
Daddy is trying to read the map
He says it can't be far.

Three, four
Open the door
We're here and at the gate.
When are the lions going to be fed?
I hope we're not too late.

Five, six
Dolphins do tricks
We all get soaking wet.
We look at the elephants, camels and bears
And a hippo I'd love for a pet.

Seven, eight
The monkeys are great
Swinging from tree to tree.
Then down some steps to the penquins' pool
To watch them having tea.

Nine, ten
Home again
As sleepy as can be.
There's so much to do
When we go to the zoo
I'm glad you came with me!

Twenty Knobbly Knees

Twenty knobbly knees	20
Nineteen fidgety fleas	19
Eighteen building bricks	18
Seventeen chirpy chicks	17
Sixteen squiggly snakes	16
Fifteen fancy cakes	15
Fourteen flying bats	14
Thirteen hanging hats	13
Twelve croaky frogs	12
Eleven slippery logs	11
Ten teddy bears	10
Nine old chairs	9
Eight twinkling stars	8
Seven racing cars	7
Six bright coats	6
Five sailing boats	5
Four favourite books	4
Three quarrelling cooks	3
Two ticking clocks	2
One odd sock	1

A Big Sum

Two, add two elephants
That makes **four** —
Elephants in a row.
Add two more, to make it **six**
How many more to go?
Add three in a line — that makes **nine**
And one more, just for fun.
TEN clumping elephants on this page —
Now that's a very big sum!

Busy Bees

One, two, three, four, five
Bumblebees around the hive
Taking nectar from each flower
Busy working hour by hour.

Six, seven, eight, nine, ten
Bumblebees fly home again
Dusting pollen from their knees
Busy buzzy bees.

Speckly Hen

Speckly Hen, lives in a barn

Lays her eggs all over the farm.

One in the meadow,

Two in the trees,

Three by the hive and the honeybees.

Four by the duckpond,

Five on a mat,

Six in the farmer's old green hat!

Ten Little Monkeys

Ten little monkeys swinging on a line,
One let go ... then there were nine.

Nine little monkeys climbing on a gate,
One slipped off ... then there were eight.

Eight little monkeys flying up to heaven,
One flew away ... then there were seven.

Seven little monkeys playing with some bricks,
One toppled over ... then there were six.

Six little monkeys going for a drive,
One got left behind ... then there were five.

Five little monkeys knocking at the door,
One wouldn't go inside … then there were four.

Four little monkeys sitting down to tea,
One felt sick … then there were three.

Three little monkeys make a sailing crew,
One fell overboard … then there were two.

Two little monkeys basking in the sun,
One got too hot … then there was one.

One little monkey standing all alone,
Went to find the other nine … then there were NONE.

Small Things

Apple pips, a drop of rain;
One button off my coat again.

Birthday candles, purple plums;
Two pink plasters on my thumbs.

Ladybirds and crawling snails;
Three little pigs with curly tails.

A tray of tarts, my favourite cup;
Four little puddles from a new-born pup.

Butterflies and grains of sand;
Five finger puppets on my hand.

Cotton reels, seashore shells;
Six bats swinging from the old church bells.

Blobs of paint, dotty spots;
Seven birds perched on the chimney pots.

House door keys, a fairy ring;
Eight sweet notes that I can sing.
(doh-ray-me-fa-so-la-te-doh)

Mewing kittens, flower seeds;
Nine bright wooden necklace beads.

Postage stamps, my bucket and spade;
Ten toy bandsmen on parade!

Pumpkin Pie

Oh my! pumpkin pie.
Make them and bake them and
Pile 'em up high.

One for a daddy,
Two for a mummy,
Three for a baby with a fat pink tummy.
Four for the boys,
Five for the girls,
Six for the child with the long dark curls.
Seven for Jack,
Eight for Jill,
Nine for the scarecrow on the hill.
Ten for the farmer's jolly wife —
She's grown pumpkins all her life!

Furry
Friends

New Chicks

Yellow chicks
Wobbly legs
Clamber out of
Crackly eggs.

Tiny beaks
Beady eyes
Fluffy feathers
Baby size.

Chirpy chicks
Little things
Huddle under
Speckled wings.

In the nest
Safe and warm
Mother keeps them
All from harm.

Three Out Walking

When Hamish MacGregor and I go out
Titus, my cat, comes too.
We walk in a line
He complains all the time —
The way that some cats do.

Hamish MacGregor keeps stopping to sniff,
Tracking the scent of a beast.
Wagging his tail,
He's hot on the trail
Of a lion ... or a beetle at least.

Hamish MacGregor is always behind,
Titus likes striding ahead;
And, hey diddle diddle
I'm in the middle
Taking them home to be fed.

The Chase

The dog chased a cat,
The cat chased a mouse
Roundabout
    and roundabout
        and roundabout the house.

The dog caught a cold,
The cat began to sneeze,
The mouse ran up
    and down about
        a chunky piece of cheese.

Pets at the Vet

Pets at the vet
Waiting,
With bandaged paws
Bumps and sores.
Ears sagging
Tails not wagging.

Three dogs and a cat,
A long-tailed rat,
All need attention,
Not to mention
A very sick snake —
Thin as a rake
Or the fish in a jar
And a budgerigar.

Waiting . . .

"Next, please," says the vet
Smiling,
And takes good care
Of each patient there.
With medicine and pills
He cures the ills
Of the dogs and the cat
And the long-tailed rat,
The very sick snake —
Thin as a rake,
And the fish in a jar
And the budgerigar.
Until,

There are no more pets
At the vet.

Aristotle Humphrey Miller

Aristotle Humphrey Miller
Found a furry caterpillar,
Watched the caterpillar crawl
Through a crack and down a wall.
Followed it along the street
Dodging in and out of feet.
Till at last it reached a drain
Never to be seen again.
Said Aristotle Humphrey Miller,
"I really liked that caterpillar."

My New Puppy

Pickle's a bundle of trouble,

He got Gran's knitting in a muddle;

Chewed a slipper and what's more

Made muddy paw marks on the floor.

So I said, "Pickle, behave! Come when I call."

Now, when he's alseep ... he's no trouble at all.

Prehistoric Pet

A little girl called Maggie

Had a mammoth, big and shaggy.

The front end of Jim

Looked grizzly and grim,

But the tail end was friendly and waggy.

My thanks to Anonymous for inspiring this version!

Hunt the Guinea Pig

Round and round the garden
Everyone look for Fred.
We've got to find my guinea pig
Before I got to bed.

Mum says, "Mind my roses!"
Dad says, "Watch the cat.
If she finds Fred before we do ...
That'll be the end of that."

Round and round the garden
We're all on hands and knees.
I know he's hiding somewhere —
Fred. Come out now, please !

Listen. I hear squeaking.
There! Behind the shed.
We all played hunt the guinea pig —
But I found Fred.

At School

Teddy
$$2 + 2 = 4$$
cat dog

The Way to School

Down the garden,
Through the gate,
Along the road,
At half-past-eight.

Round the corner,
Up the street,
Here comes Amy,
Max and Pete.

Right at the station,
Left by the shops,
Cross the road
When the traffic stops.

The school bell clangs.
The clock strikes nine ...
Run to the playground,
Just in time!

Team Games

Last week I joined the Blue team
And strange to tell, but true,
The other teams all won a race —
Every team but Blue.

Today I ran in the Red team,
And then Miss Ellis said,
"Well done Yellows, Greens and Blues!
Bad luck, those in Red."

So now I don't know what to do,
Which colour should I choose?
Whatever colour team I'M in ...
That colour seems to lose!

Sports Day

I went in for the sack race,
I was doing all right until
Josh bumped into Lizzie
And I fell over Bill.

We almost came first in the three-legged race,
Me and Daisy Peep.
Then our legs got muddled up somehow,
And we landed up in a heap.

But my best race was running,
Bang! went the starting gun.
I ran like the wind to the finishing line
And everyone cheered, "You've WON!"

A Quiet Corner

There's a quiet corner in our classroom
Where I can curl up like a kitten on the cushions
To listen to a story
Or take a book from the shelf
And read one for myself,
Quietly.

School Rules

One at a time

Keep in line,

Don't talk

Walk!

Don't run

Have fun but

Don't bully

Wear your woolly,

Shut the door

Sit on the floor and

Don't wriggle

Or giggle at prayers

Don't play on the stairs

Stop making that noise and ...

Be good girls and boys!

The School Play

I'm in the school play this Christmas,
I've got an important part;
So I'm learning and learning and learning my lines
Until I can say them by heart.

When I go on stage I'll be nervous,
I'm sure I'll forget what to say.
You see I'm the front of the pantomime horse —
"Neigh, neigh, neigh, neigh, NEIGH!"

Dinosaur Spellings

Dinosaurs have such strange names.

They're long and not easy to spell

like,

STEGOSAURUS

TRICERATOPS

PTERODACTYL

and

TYRANNOSAURUS

as well.

But dinosaur names are **special**

So I'm trying my hardest to spell,

STEGOSAURUS

TRICERATOPS

PTERODACTYL

and

TYRANNOSAURUS

as well!

A Scary Bunch

The Giant

Fee, fi, fo, fum,
A giant was here in town.
His great big feet
Clumped down our street,
Knocking the houses down.

Fee, fi, fo, fum,
The giant had come for ME.
His mouth opened wide,
He popped me inside
And crunched my bones for tea.

Fee, fi, fo, fum,
You must have heard me scream.
"You're safe in bed,"
My father said.
"That giant was in your DREAM."

Under My Bed

Something lives under my bed
It was there again last night,
Grunting and growling like anything —
It gave me an awful fright.

Does it have hairy legs,
With feet and terrible claws?
Will it start to chew me up
In its slobbering toothy jaws?

This morning I felt brave
So Elephant, Tiger and me
All looked carefully under the bed
To see what it could be ...

But there was nothing there.

A Monstrous Recipe

Buckets of beetles,

Tubs of toads,

Smelly fishheads — loads and loads.

Lumpy gravy,

Mouldy stew,

Stir it up with a worm or two.

Put in a pot.

Cook for a week ...

Now you know what monsters eat!

Ghost Train

We went for a ride on the ghost train,
Dominic, Gemma and me.
We screamed going into a tunnel,
It was scary as can be.

A skeleton glowed in the darkness,
Spiders dangled from threads,
The train rattled into a churchyard
And ghosts flew over our heads.

The haunted house was spooky —
A vampire grinned with glee.
It opened its fangs to take a bite …
From Dominic, Gemma and me.

Then we raced into the sunshine,
We all looked ghostly white.
And we said, "That was **FANTASTIC** —
We've all have a wonderful fright!"

72

My Secret Monster

I know a secret cupboard
Where creepy crawlies hide.
And when I'm feeling very brave
I take a peep inside
To see the scary monster
With a hundred hairy legs,
And eyes the size of apple pies
In two enormous heads.
But should that monster see me
And turn his heads my way ...
I'd shut that secret cupboard door
And run a mile away.

Very quickly.

Spotted Shingly Shangly Beasts

Spotted Shingly Shangly Beasts
Are seaweed green and scaly.
They gobble up enormous feasts
Of cod and herring daily.

They like to sleep in rocky caves
(I've often heard them snore);
Or dip their toes and tails in waves
That splash upon the shore.

And sometimes when the moon is bright
I have seen them prancing —
Across the sands, all through the night,
These curious beasts go dancing.

I Know a Tumbly House

I know a tumbly house
With a creaky little door,
Where a squeaky little mouse
Lives below a rotten floor.

Inside those crumbly walls
There's a musty little room,
Where a dusty little ghost
Hums a mournful little tune.

At least that's what I'm **told** is there,
So one day when I'm bold, I'll dare
To peep inside that spooky house
And see the ghost myself,

But not just yet …

Green-eyed Witches

Down in the woods where the trees are bare
And twigs scritch scratch to tangle your hair,
There in the light of a sliver of moon
The green-eyed witches sit and croon
In tattered capes and pointed hats
Around a cauldron filled with bats.
They fly on broomsticks way up high
To sweep dark cobwebs from the sky,
And catch giant spiders for a brew ...
At Halloween — they might snatch you!

Plain Silly

Ladywig and Earbird

A ladywig and earbird
Were crawling up the wall.
Said the earbird to the ladywig,
"I don't feel right at all."

Said the ladywig, "I feel odd too
Now this may seem absurd,
But at the top
Our names we'll swap,
EARWIG and LADYBIRD."

"You've changed my life!"
The earwig said,
"I feel a different bug."
Then the earwig gave the ladybird
A great big buggy hug.

Colourful Moods

When grown-ups say, "I'm feeling **BLUE**,"
It really means they're sad.
Or if they say, "I'm in the **PINK**,"
They're healthy, bright and glad.

It's strange the things that people say
Like, envy turns you **GREEN**.
Or someone's turned a ghostly **WHITE**
At frightening things they've seen.

It's odd the colours grown-ups go
Or say that they have been.
I stay the colour of my skin
Whatever mood I'm in.

Saturday Sweets

Creamy eggs,
Sugar mice,
Chewy toffee bars;
Liquorice loops,
Chocolate chips,
Fizzy sherbet stars.
Gummy snakes and
Dinosaurs,
Lollies on a stick,

We eat them all on Saturday
And Sunday — we feel sick!

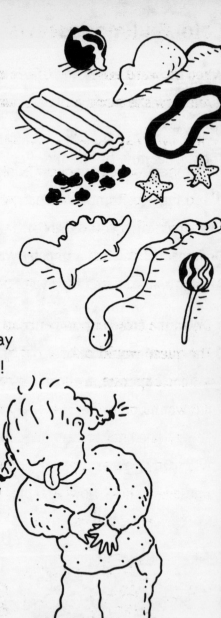

The Queen of Hearts

You've heard about the Queen of Hearts
And how she made a plate of tarts?

That wasn't all the queen could cook,
She often took her cookery book
And opened it to find the page
Where stuffings were, of thyme and sage
With which to stuff a bird or two,
When she had nothing else to do.

Or, with a crown upon her head
The queen would bake a loaf of bread,
A treacle sponge, a chocolate cake.
But what a mess the queen did make.
She left the kitchen sink piled high
With dirty pots and pans — oh my!
And every sticky bowl and cup,
She NEVER did the washing up!

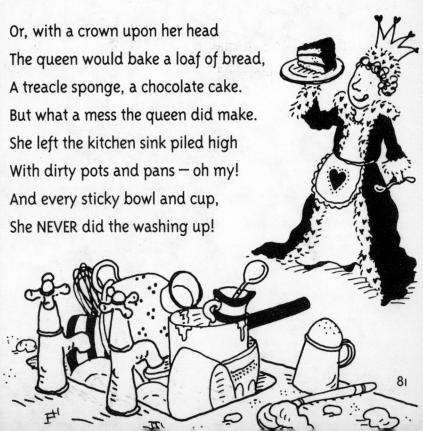

Tooth Fairies

Why do the fairies take our teeth?
It does seem very funny,
To take a tooth that's fallen out
And leave behind some money.

Jumpy Custard

If all the world was ice-cream
And all the seas were mustard
And all the skies were apple pies,
There wouldn't be any custard.

Which would be a pity because,

Frogs love it!
Even when it's lumpy.
They eat it hot
They eat it cold
They eat it when it's NINE DAYS OLD!
Custard makes them ... jumpy.

Bathroom Nonsense

Wash your hair with custard,

Scrub your face with ink,

Clean your teeth with cream cheese ...

Then go to bed in the sink!

Roger the Robot

Roger is a robot
With tinny hands and feet,
A super brain and saucer ears
Makes Roger quite complete.
Though he's supersonic clever
And can speak with metal lips,
All he eats for breakfast
Is a bowl of micro chips.

Little Miss Locket

Little Miss Locket, jumped in a rocket
The rocket blew up, so she rode in a cup
The cup had a crack, so she hopped in a sack
The sack was too loose, so she sat on a goose
The goose made a fuss, so she got on a bus
And spent all week at the TERMINUS.

The World
Around Us

A Colourful World

1. Sea swirling,
   waves curling
   blue.

2. Desert shifting,
   sand drifting
   yellow.

3. Seeds sowing,
   grass mowing
   green.

4. Fire burning,
   flames turning
   orange.

5. Wind blowing,
   clouds growing
   black.

6. Cold morning,
   snow storming
   white.

7. Sun setting,
   sky getting
   red.

Globe Trotting

Rushing off to Russia,
Skipping down to France,
Hopping round America
If I have half a chance.
Popping into Africa, India and then
China and Australia,
There and back again!

Opposites

Fast as a spaceship,
    slow as a snail,
Big as a dinosaur,
    small as a nail.
Fierce as a tiger,
    gentle as a lamb,
Sour as a lemon,
    sweet as jam.
Dry as a desert,
    wet as the sea,
Square as a house,
    round as a pea.
Cool as a cave,
    warm as toast,

Noisy as a road drill,
    quiet as a ghost.
Strong as an ox,
    weak as a kitten
Hard as a rock,
    soft as a mitten.
Dark as a tunnel,
    light as the moon,
Night time midnight,
    day time noon.
Tall as a giant,
    short as an elf,
Crooked as a mountain path
    straight as a shelf ..

**The world is full of opposites,
so think of some yourself!**

How High is the Sky?

How high is the sky?
Does it stop at the top of the ozone layer,
Somewhere up there, in the stratosphere?
If not,
Then what?

Big Things

Jumbo jets and
Fairground wheels,
A bright hot-air balloon;
Planet Earth,
The pyramids,
A rocket to the moon.

Elephants and
Ocean ships,
Rocky mountains high;
A city full of busy streets,
The dark and starry sky.

Dinosaurs and
Dumper trucks,
A giant forest tree;
The world around seems very BIG
To someone small like me.

Things People Do

Farmers grow the crops we eat,
Bakers make us bread,
Fisher folk go out to sea
While we are warm in bed.
Authors write the books we read,
Artists paint and draw,
Photographers take photographs,
Policemen keep the law.
Teachers help us learn at school,
Doctors make us well,
Workers in a factory
Make things to buy and sell.
An astronaut in Outer Space,
A keeper in the zoo,
When you grow up, what will you be?
There's SOMETHING you can do!

On the Move

Traffic on the motorway,
Jets in the air,
Liners on the ocean waves
Sailing somewhere.

Trains on the railway track,
Vans on the road,
A motor-car transporter —
With a double load.

Buses in the High Street,
Barges on the river,
Motor-cycle messengers
With parcels to deliver.

Police cars in a hurry,
Tankers going slow ...
All of them are on the move,
Now think of some YOU know!

Circles

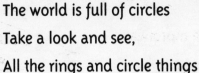

The world is full of circles
Take a look and see,
All the rings and circle things
Surrounding you and me.

Cups and saucers
Plates and bowls
The iris in your eye;
The letter 'O'
A roundabout
The full moon in the sky.

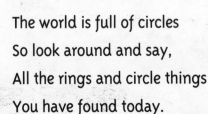

A hoop to spin
A ring to wear
A record you can play;
Four rubber tyres
A steering wheel
To turn and drive away.

The world is full of circles
So look around and say,
All the rings and circle things
You have found today.

A Crumb

There's a crumb on my plate ...

The plate is on a table
The table is in a room
The room is in a house
The house is in a street
The street is in a town
The town is in a country
The country is in the world.

And if the world were a plate ...
that tiny crumb would be me.